To Helen Love Mummy & Daddy

SUPER-QUICK
ADDING
and
SUBTRACTING
in your head

by Norman D Lock
cover illustration by Peter O

D1451334

Ladybird

Ladybird books are widely available, but in case of difficulty may be ordered by post
or telephone from: Ladybird Books – Cash Sales Department
Littlegate Road Paignton Devon TQ3 3BE Telephone 01803 554761

Published by Ladybird Books Ltd Loughborough Leicestershire UK
Ladybird Books Inc Auburn Maine 04210 USA

Test 1a

1. $1 + 3 = *$
2. $2 + 1 = *$
3. $3 + 3 = *$
4. $1 + 4 = *$
5. $4 + 2 = *$
6. $1 + 1 = *$
7. $2 + 5 = *$
8. $3 + 5 = *$
9. $3 + 1 = *$
10. $1 + 7 = *$
11. $2 + 2 = *$
12. $1 + 5 = *$
13. $3 + 4 = *$
14. $2 + 3 = *$
15. $3 + 0 = *$
16. $4 + 3 = *$
17. $2 + 7 = *$
18. $4 + 4 = *$
19. $3 + 2 = *$
20. $3 + 6 = *$

Do not write in this space.

Place a sheet of scrap paper here and write your answers on that.

Always remembe to time yourself for each test.

Write your score out of 20 and your time in minutes and seconds on the Record Sheet at the back of this book.

Test 1b

1 7 − 3 = *

2 4 − 2 = *

3 6 − 4 = *

4 7 − 2 = *

5 9 − 7 = *

6 5 − 2 = *

7 6 − 3 = *

8 8 − 5 = *

9 7 − 4 = *

10 9 − 6 = *

11 5 − 3 = *

12 4 − 1 = *

13 4 − 3 = *

14 3 − 0 = *

15 8 − 1 = *

16 5 − 4 = *

17 8 − 4 = *

18 6 − 1 = *

19 3 − 2 = *

20 2 − 1 = *

Do not write in this space.

Place a sheet of scrap paper here and write your answers on that.

Always remember to time yourself for each test.

Write your score out of 20 and your time in minutes and seconds on the Record Sheet at the back of this book.

Test 1c

1. $* + 2 = 6$

2. $8 - * = 5$

3. $1 + * = 6$

4. $* - 3 = 4$

5. $* + 3 = 4$

6. $7 - * = 5$

7. $3 + * = 6$

8. $* - 4 = 4$

9. $* + 2 = 4$

10. $8 - * = 1$

11. $3 + * = 5$

12. $* - 6 = 3$

13. $* + 1 = 4$

14. $3 - * = 1$

15. $4 + * = 7$

16. $* - 4 = 1$

17. $* + 1 = 2$

18. $5 - * = 3$

19. $2 + * = 7$

20. $* - 0 = 3$

Do not write in this space.

Place a sheet of scrap paper here and write your answers on that.

Always remember to time yourself for each test.

Write your score out of 20 and your time in minutes and seconds on the Record Sheet at the back of this book.

Test 2a

1. $1 + 6 = *$

2. $4 + 5 = *$

3. $5 + 1 = *$

4. $2 + 6 = *$

5. $3 + 7 = *$

6. $5 + 2 = *$

7. $4 + 1 = *$

8. $5 + 5 = *$

9. $2 + 4 = *$

10. $1 + 2 = *$

11. $4 + 0 = *$

12. $5 + 4 = *$

13. $6 + 2 = *$

14. $1 + 9 = *$

15. $7 + 2 = *$

16. $4 + 6 = *$

17. $3 + 3 = *$

18. $6 + 1 = *$

19. $1 + 8 = *$

20. $6 + 4 = *$

Do not write in this space.

Place a sheet of scrap paper here and write your answers on that.

Always remember to time yourself for each test.

Write your score out of 20 and your time in minutes and seconds on the Record Sheet at the back of this book.

Test 2b

1   $10 - 5 = *$

2   $4 - 0 = *$

3   $8 - 6 = *$

4   $5 - 1 = *$

5   $8 - 2 = *$

6   $10 - 6 = *$

7   $7 - 1 = *$

8   $9 - 4 = *$

9   $7 - 6 = *$

10   $3 - 1 = *$

11   $7 - 2 = *$

12   $6 - 3 = *$

13   $10 - 4 = *$

14   $9 - 5 = *$

15   $6 - 2 = *$

16   $10 - 1 = *$

17   $9 - 8 = *$

18   $10 - 3 = *$

19   $9 - 2 = *$

20   $6 - 5 = *$

Do not write in this space.

Place a sheet of scrap paper here and write your answers on that.

Always remember to time yourself for each test.

Write your score out of 20 and your time in minutes and seconds on the Record Sheet at the back of this book.

Test 2c

1. $* + 2 = 7$

2. $6 - * = 2$

3. $5 + * = 9$

4. $* - 2 = 6$

5. $* + 4 = 4$

6. $9 - * = 2$

7. $5 + * = 10$

8. $* - 4 = 6$

9. $* + 5 = 9$

10. $10 - * = 1$

11. $1 + * = 3$

12. $* - 1 = 8$

13. $* + 4 = 5$

14. $8 - * = 6$

15. $7 + * = 10$

16. $* - 3 = 0$

17. $* + 1 = 6$

18. $7 - * = 1$

19. $6 + * = 10$

20. $* - 6 = 1$

Do not write in this space.

Place a sheet of scrap paper here and write your answers on that.

Always remember to time yourself for each test.

Write your score out of 20 and your time in minutes and seconds on the Record Sheet at the back of this book.

Test 3a

1 4 + 3 = *

2 5 + 3 = *

3 2 + 8 = *

4 6 + 3 = *

5 2 + 5 = *

6 3 + 7 = *

7 7 + 2 = *

8 6 + 4 = *

9 7 + 1 = *

10 8 + 2 = *

11 4 + 5 = *

12 3 + 8 = *

13 6 + 6 = *

14 3 + 5 = *

15 2 + 10 = *

16 7 + 4 = *

17 3 + 2 = *

18 7 + 0 = *

19 5 + 6 = *

20 2 + 6 = *

Do not write in this space.

Place a sheet of scrap paper here and write your answers on that.

Always remember to time yourself for each test.

Write your score out of 20 and your time in minutes and seconds on the Record Sheet at the back of this book.

Test 3b

1. $9 - 3 = *$

2. $5 - 2 = *$

3. $10 - 7 = *$

4. $7 - 3 = *$

5. $8 - 1 = *$

6. $11 - 3 = *$

7. $8 - 5 = *$

8. $8 - 2 = *$

9. $10 - 2 = *$

10. $9 - 4 = *$

11. $12 - 6 = *$

12. $11 - 4 = *$

13. $9 - 7 = *$

14. $7 - 2 = *$

15. $12 - 10 = *$

16. $7 - 0 = *$

17. $10 - 8 = *$

18. $8 - 3 = *$

19. $10 - 4 = *$

20. $11 - 5 = *$

Do not write in this space.

Place a sheet of scrap paper here and write your answers on that.

Always remember to time yourself for each test.

Write your score out of 20 and your time in minutes and seconds on the Record Sheet at the back of this book.

Test 3c

1 $* + 3 = 8$

2 $9 - * = 4$

3 $2 + * = 7$

4 $* - 2 = 8$

5 $* + 6 = 11$

6 $8 - * = 5$

7 $3 + * = 10$

8 $* - 6 = 2$

9 $* + 3 = 9$

10 $6 - * = 0$

11 $2 + * = 10$

12 $* - 4 = 7$

13 $* + 2 = 9$

14 $5 - * = 2$

15 $2 + * = 12$

16 $* - 8 = 3$

17 $* + 0 = 7$

18 $8 - * = 7$

19 $3 + * = 7$

20 $* - 4 = 6$

Do not write in this space.

Place a sheet of scrap paper here and write your answers on that.

Always remember to time yourself for each test.

Write your score out of 20 and your time in minutes and seconds on the Record Sheet at the back of this book.

Test 4a

1. $7 + 3 = *$

2. $4 + 2 = *$

3. $2 + 9 = *$

4. $4 + 8 = *$

5. $2 + 3 = *$

6. $3 + 6 = *$

7. $7 + 5 = *$

8. $4 + 4 = *$

9. $8 + 1 = *$

10. $9 + 2 = *$

11. $2 + 8 = *$

12. $7 + 6 = *$

13. $4 + 7 = *$

14. $2 + 11 = *$

15. $6 + 5 = *$

16. $2 + 4 = *$

17. $10 + 3 = *$

18. $3 + 9 = *$

19. $6 + 2 = *$

20. $9 + 3 = *$

Do not write in this space.

Place a sheet of scrap paper here and write your answers on that.

Always remember to time yourself for each test.

Write your score out of 20 and your time in minutes and seconds on the Record Sheet at the back of this book.

Test 4b

1. $8 - 4 = *$

2. $11 - 2 = *$

3. $13 - 6 = *$

4. $6 - 2 = *$

5. $12 - 9 = *$

6. $9 - 1 = *$

7. $10 - 3 = *$

8. $11 - 4 = *$

9. $13 - 2 = *$

10. $8 - 6 = *$

11. $12 - 4 = *$

12. $11 - 6 = *$

13. $10 - 8 = *$

14. $6 - 4 = *$

15. $12 - 3 = *$

16. $13 - 10 = *$

17. $11 - 9 = *$

18. $5 - 2 = *$

19. $9 - 3 = *$

20. $12 - 5 = *$

Do not write in this space.

Place a sheet of scrap paper here and write your answers on that.

Always remember to time yourself for each test.

Write your score out of 20 and your time in minutes and seconds on the Record Sheet at the back of this book.

Test 4c

1 $* + 4 = 8$

2 $12 - * = 4$

3 $2 + * = 11$

4 $* - 5 = 7$

5 $* + 6 = 13$

6 $11 - * = 6$

7 $6 + * = 8$

8 $* - 2 = 8$

9 $* + 3 = 5$

10 $13 - * = 11$

11 $4 + * = 6$

12 $* - 2 = 9$

13 $* + 3 = 10$

14 $4 - * = 2$

15 $9 + * = 12$

16 $* - 3 = 6$

17 $* + 4 = 11$

18 $12 - * = 3$

19 $8 + * = 9$

20 $* - 10 = 3$

Do not write in this space.

Place a sheet of scrap paper here and write your answers on that.

Always remember to time yourself for each test.

Write your score out of 20 and your time in minutes and seconds on the Record Sheet at the back of this book.

Test 5a

1. $8 + 3 = *$

2. $2 + 2 = *$

3. $5 + 3 = *$

4. $1 + 10 = *$

5. $4 + 9 = *$

6. $4 + 6 = *$

7. $1 + 11 = *$

8. $9 + 1 = *$

9. $5 + 7 = *$

10. $3 + 4 = *$

11. $6 + 5 = *$

12. $9 + 4 = *$

13. $6 + 6 = *$

14. $11 + 2 = *$

15. $2 + 7 = *$

16. $5 + 8 = *$

17. $3 + 8 = *$

18. $10 + 2 = *$

19. $5 + 4 = *$

20. $7 + 3 = *$

Do not write in this space.

Place a sheet of scrap paper here and write your answers on that.

Always remember to time yourself for each test.

Write your score out of 20 and your time in minutes and seconds on the Record Sheet at the back of this book.

Test 5b

1. $12 - 6 = *$
2. $10 - 4 = *$
3. $8 - 3 = *$
4. $11 - 3 = *$
5. $9 - 4 = *$
6. $12 - 5 = *$
7. $11 - 10 = *$
8. $4 - 2 = *$
9. $11 - 5 = *$
10. $9 - 2 = *$
11. $10 - 3 = *$
12. $12 - 1 = *$
13. $13 - 9 = *$
14. $7 - 3 = *$
15. $13 - 5 = *$
16. $10 - 1 = *$
17. $12 - 2 = *$
18. $13 - 11 = *$
19. $11 - 8 = *$
20. $13 - 4 = *$

Do not write in this space.

Place a sheet of scrap paper here and write your answers on that.

Always remember to time yourself for each test.

Write your score out of 20 and your time in minutes and seconds on the Record Sheet at the back of this book.

Test 5c

1 * + 3 = 8

2 12 - * = 6

3 5 + * = 13

4 * - 7 = 5

5 * + 5 = 11

6 10 - * = 6

7 2 + * = 9

8 * - 3 = 7

9 * + 3 = 11

10 13 - * = 9

11 2 + * = 4

12 * - 4 = 5

13 * + 9 = 10

14 12 - * = 10

15 3 + * = 7

16 * - 2 = 11

17 * + 1 = 12

18 11 - * = 8

19 9 + * = 12

20 * - 9 = 4

Do not write in this space.

Place a sheet of scrap paper here and write your answers on that.

Always remember to time yourself for each test.

Write your score out of 20 and your time in minutes and seconds on the Record Sheet at the back of this book.

Test 6a

1. $5 + 5 = *$

2. $8 + 6 = *$

3. $3 + 10 = *$

4. $8 + 4 = *$

5. $3 + 11 = *$

6. $3 + 3 = *$

7. $8 + 2 = *$

8. $3 + 9 = *$

9. $6 + 8 = *$

10. $4 + 7 = *$

11. $9 + 2 = *$

12. $6 + 7 = *$

13. $7 + 7 = *$

14. $5 + 2 = *$

15. $9 + 5 = *$

16. $2 + 9 = *$

17. $8 + 5 = *$

18. $10 + 4 = *$

19. $6 + 1 = *$

20. $4 + 8 = *$

Do not write in
this space.

Place a sheet of
scrap paper here
and write your
answers on that.

Always remember
to time yourself
for each test.

Write your score
out of 20 and
your time in
minutes and
seconds on the
Record Sheet
at the back of
this book.

Test 6b

1 7 − 1 = *

2 11 − 7 = *

3 6 − 3 = *

4 14 − 6 = *

5 11 − 2 = *

6 12 − 3 = *

7 7 − 2 = *

8 14 − 7 = *

9 13 − 8 = *

10 14 − 8 = *

11 11 − 9 = *

12 13 − 3 = *

13 12 − 4 = *

14 10 − 2 = *

15 13 − 7 = *

16 14 − 5 = *

17 12 − 8 = *

18 14 − 3 = *

19 10 − 5 = *

20 14 − 9 = *

Do not write in this space.

Place a sheet of scrap paper here and write your answers on that.

Always remember to time yourself for each test.

Write your score out of 20 and your time in minutes and seconds on the Record Sheet at the back of this book.

Test 6c

1. $* + 2 = 7$

2. $12 - * = 4$

3. $6 + * = 14$

4. $* - 8 = 5$

5. $* + 2 = 11$

6. $10 - * = 8$

7. $3 + * = 12$

8. $* - 5 = 5$

9. $* + 6 = 13$

10. $11 - * = 4$

11. $3 + * = 6$

12. $* - 6 = 8$

13. $* + 7 = 14$

14. $7 - * = 1$

15. $3 + * = 13$

16. $* - 9 = 5$

17. $* + 11 = 14$

18. $12 - * = 8$

19. $2 + * = 11$

20. $* - 10 = 4$

Do not write in this space.

Place a sheet of scrap paper here and write your answers on that.

Always remember to time yourself for each test.

Write your score out of 20 and your time in minutes and seconds on the Record Sheet at the back of this book.

Test 7a

1 7 + 4 = *

2 8 + 5 = *

3 6 + 4 = *

4 5 + 9 = *

5 6 + 3 = *

6 9 + 4 = *

7 5 + 10 = *

8 6 + 7 = *

9 3 + 7 = *

10 2 + 12 = *

11 11 + 3 = *

12 8 + 7 = *

13 5 + 7 = *

14 9 + 6 = *

15 4 + 9 = *

16 5 + 2 = *

17 3 + 12 = *

18 2 + 11 = *

19 11 + 4 = *

20 5 + 6 = *

Do not write in
this space.

Place a sheet of
scrap paper here
and write your
answers on that

Always remember
to time yourself
for each test.

Write your score
out of 20 and
your time in
minutes and
seconds on the
Record Sheet
at the back of
this book.

Test 7b

1. $13 - 6 = *$

2. $10 - 4 = *$

3. $14 - 3 = *$

4. $13 - 4 = *$

5. $9 - 3 = *$

6. $11 - 7 = *$

7. $12 - 5 = *$

8. $15 - 7 = *$

9. $14 - 2 = *$

10. $15 - 10 = *$

11. $13 - 11 = *$

12. $11 - 6 = *$

13. $15 - 3 = *$

14. $14 - 5 = *$

15. $10 - 7 = *$

16. $15 - 6 = *$

17. $15 - 11 = *$

18. $7 - 2 = *$

19. $13 - 9 = *$

20. $14 - 9 = *$

Do not write in this space.

Place a sheet of scrap paper here and write your answers on that.

Always remember to time yourself for each test.

Write your score out of 20 and your time in minutes and seconds on the Record Sheet at the back of this book.

Test 7c

1. $* + 3 = 9$

2. $13 - * = 7$

3. $6 + * = 10$

4. $* - 8 = 7$

5. $* + 6 = 15$

6. $10 - * = 3$

7. $2 + * = 14$

8. $* - 4 = 11$

9. $* + 2 = 7$

10. $12 - * = 7$

11. $5 + * = 14$

12. $* - 4 = 9$

13. $* + 4 = 11$

14. $13 - * = 5$

15. $3 + * = 15$

16. $* - 9 = 4$

17. $* + 11 = 14$

18. $11 - * = 6$

19. $2 + * = 13$

20. $* - 5 = 10$

Do not write in this space.

Place a sheet of scrap paper here and write your answers on that.

Always remember to time yourself for each test.

Write your score out of 20 and your time in minutes and seconds on the Record Sheet at the back of this book.

Test 8a

1. $8 + 8 = *$

2. $4 + 10 = *$

3. $7 + 5 = *$

4. $12 + 2 = *$

5. $3 + 13 = *$

6. $8 + 2 = *$

7. $11 + 5 = *$

8. $4 + 6 = *$

9. $2 + 13 = *$

10. $7 + 7 = *$

11. $5 + 11 = *$

12. $9 + 5 = *$

13. $8 + 3 = *$

14. $7 + 6 = *$

15. $4 + 11 = *$

16. $6 + 10 = *$

17. $6 + 6 = *$

18. $6 + 9 = *$

19. $9 + 7 = *$

20. $12 + 3 = *$

Do not write in this space.

Place a sheet of scrap paper here and write your answers on that.

Always remember to time yourself for each test.

Write your score out of 20 and your time in minutes and seconds on the Record Sheet at the back of this book.

Test 8b

1 $14 - 7 = *$

2 $16 - 8 = *$

3 $16 - 11 = *$

4 $15 - 4 = *$

5 $12 - 6 = *$

6 $16 - 7 = *$

7 $13 - 6 = *$

8 $15 - 2 = *$

9 $10 - 8 = *$

10 $13 - 7 = *$

11 $10 - 4 = *$

12 $11 - 3 = *$

13 $15 - 12 = *$

14 $16 - 6 = *$

15 $14 - 2 = *$

16 $16 - 5 = *$

17 $15 - 9 = *$

18 $14 - 5 = *$

19 $16 - 13 = *$

20 $14 - 4 = *$

Do not write in this space.

Place a sheet of scrap paper here and write your answers on that.

Always remember to time yourself for each test.

Write your score out of 20 and your time in minutes and seconds on the Record Sheet at the back of this book.

Test 8c

1 $* + 2 = 10$

2 $14 - * = 9$

3 $4 + * = 10$

4 $* - 7 = 7$

5 $* + 3 = 11$

6 $13 - * = 6$

7 $6 + * = 12$

8 $* - 9 = 7$

9 $* + 3 = 15$

10 $16 - * = 5$

11 $3 + * = 16$

12 $* - 6 = 9$

13 $* + 5 = 12$

14 $15 - * = 2$

15 $8 + * = 16$

16 $* - 4 = 11$

17 $* + 2 = 12$

18 $16 - * = 6$

19 $11 + * = 15$

20 $* - 10 = 4$

Do not write in this space.

Place a sheet of scrap paper here and write your answers on that.

Always remember to time yourself for each test.

Write your score out of 20 and your time in minutes and seconds on the Record Sheet at the back of this book.

Test 9a

1 $5 + 9 = *$

2 $8 + 3 = *$

3 $5 + 5 = *$

4 $7 + 9 = *$

5 $8 + 7 = *$

6 $5 + 8 = *$

7 $12 + 4 = *$

8 $4 + 8 = *$

9 $11 + 2 = *$

10 $4 + 12 = *$

11 $10 + 5 = *$

12 $2 + 14 = *$

13 $9 + 3 = *$

14 $8 + 6 = *$

15 $13 + 2 = *$

16 $10 + 6 = *$

17 $6 + 11 = *$

18 $9 + 8 = *$

19 $7 + 6 = *$

20 $11 + 6 = *$

Do not write in this space.

Place a sheet of scrap paper here and write your answers on that.

Always remember to time yourself for each test.

Write your score out of 20 and your time in minutes and seconds on the Record Sheet at the back of this book.

Test 9b

1. $16 - 4 = *$

2. $10 - 5 = *$

3. $13 - 2 = *$

4. $12 - 9 = *$

5. $15 - 2 = *$

6. $17 - 8 = *$

7. $15 - 7 = *$

8. $11 - 3 = *$

9. $14 - 6 = *$

10. $13 - 7 = *$

11. $13 - 5 = *$

12. $16 - 7 = *$

13. $17 - 11 = *$

14. $15 - 5 = *$

15. $12 - 4 = *$

16. $17 - 11 = *$

17. $16 - 12 = *$

18. $14 - 5 = *$

19. $16 - 10 = *$

20. $16 - 14 = *$

Do not write in this space.

Place a sheet of scrap paper here and write your answers on that.

Always remember to time yourself for each test.

Write your score out of 20 and your time in minutes and seconds on the Record Sheet at the back of this book.

Test 9c

1   * + 6 = 13

2   16 − * = 9

3   4 + * = 12

4   * − 5 = 8

5   * + 4 = 16

6   15 − * = 7

7   5 + * = 10

8   * − 6 = 8

9   * + 6 = 17

10 15 − * = 13

11 4 + * = 16

12 * − 8 = 9

13 * + 3 = 11

14 14 − * = 6

15 11 + * = 17

16 * − 9 = 3

17 * + 2 = 13

18 16 − * = 2

19 10 + * = 15

20 * − 6 = 10

Do not write in
this space.

Place a sheet of
scrap paper here
and write your
answers on that.

Always remembe
to time yourself
for each test.

Write your score
out of 20 and
your time in
minutes and
seconds on the
Record Sheet
at the back of
this book.

Test 10a

1   8 + 9 = *

2   4 + 11 = *

3   5 + 7 = *

4   8 + 8 = *

5   12 + 5 = *

6   9 + 6 = *

7   3 + 11 = *

8   3 + 14 = *

9   7 + 7 = *

10 10 + 4 = *

11 5 + 11 = *

12 13 + 4 = *

13 6 + 8 = *

14 7 + 10 = *

15 9 + 9 = *

16 11 + 4 = *

17 4 + 9 = *

18 5 + 12 = *

19 6 + 5 = *

20 9 + 5 = *

Do not write in this space.

Place a sheet of scrap paper here and write your answers on that.

Always remember to time yourself for each test.

Write your score out of 20 and your time in minutes and seconds on the Record Sheet at the back of this book.

Test 10b

1. $16 - 8 = *$

2. $17 - 13 = *$

3. $14 - 10 = *$

4. $17 - 3 = *$

5. $18 - 9 = *$

6. $13 - 9 = *$

7. $14 - 5 = *$

8. $17 - 9 = *$

9. $14 - 7 = *$

10. $17 - 7 = *$

11. $15 - 11 = *$

12. $15 - 6 = *$

13. $17 - 12 = *$

14. $11 - 6 = *$

15. $16 - 11 = *$

16. $14 - 6 = *$

17. $15 - 4 = *$

18. $17 - 5 = *$

19. $14 - 11 = *$

20. $13 - 5 = *$

Do not write in this space.

Place a sheet of scrap paper here and write your answers on that.

Always remember to time yourself for each test.

Write your score out of 20 and your time in minutes and seconds on the Record Sheet at the back of this book.

Test 10c

1 $* + 6 = 15$

2 $12 - * = 5$

3 $5 + * = 16$

4 $* - 8 = 6$

5 $* + 5 = 11$

6 $16 - * = 8$

7 $10 + * = 14$

8 $* - 9 = 8$

9 $* + 14 = 17$

10 $18 - * = 9$

11 $12 + * = 17$

12 $* - 5 = 9$

13 $* + 9 = 13$

14 $17 - * = 14$

15 $11 + * = 15$

16 $* - 5 = 12$

17 $* + 4 = 15$

18 $14 - * = 7$

19 $7 + * = 17$

20 $* - 9 = 6$

Do not write in this space.

Place a sheet of scrap paper here and write your answers on that.

Always remember to time yourself for each test.

Write your score out of 20 and your time in minutes and seconds on the Record Sheet at the back of this book.

Test 11a

1 11 + 3 = *

2 6 + 9 = *

3 15 + 3 = *

4 10 + 7 = *

5 2 + 12 = *

6 13 + 2 = *

7 5 + 12 = *

8 13 + 4 = *

9 8 + 6 = *

10 4 + 14 = *

11 7 + 9 = *

12 4 + 11 = *

13 5 + 13 = *

14 12 + 7 = *

15 6 + 12 = *

16 7 + 8 = *

17 7 + 5 = *

18 3 + 13 = *

19 12 + 3 = *

20 8 + 7 = *

Do not write in this space.

Place a sheet of scrap paper here and write your answers on that.

Always remember to time yourself for each test.

Write your score out of 20 and your time in minutes and seconds on the Record Sheet at the back of this book.

Test 11b

1. $15 - 7 = *$

2. $14 - 6 = *$

3. $14 - 12 = *$

4. $16 - 9 = *$

5. $17 - 5 = *$

6. $14 - 3 = *$

7. $18 - 5 = *$

8. $15 - 3 = *$

9. $15 - 13 = *$

10. $15 - 9 = *$

11. $18 - 12 = *$

12. $17 - 10 = *$

13. $15 - 11 = *$

14. $19 - 12 = *$

15. $12 - 7 = *$

16. $15 - 8 = *$

17. $17 - 4 = *$

18. $18 - 15 = *$

19. $16 - 3 = *$

20. $18 - 4 = *$

Do not write in this space.

Place a sheet of scrap paper here and write your answers on that.

Always remember to time yourself for each test.

Write your score out of 20 and your time in minutes and seconds on the Record Sheet at the back of this book.

Test 11c

1. $* + 5 = 12$

2. $15 - * = 2$

3. $7 + * = 16$

4. $* - 6 = 8$

5. $* + 12 = 15$

6. $17 - * = 5$

7. $5 + * = 18$

8. $* - 13 = 4$

9. $* + 7 = 15$

10. $17 - * = 10$

11. $4 + * = 18$

12. $* - 6 = 12$

13. $* + 3 = 14$

14. $15 - * = 8$

15. $6 + * = 15$

16. $* - 12 = 7$

17. $* + 3 = 16$

18. $15 - * = 4$

19. $2 + * = 14$

20. $* - 3 = 15$

Do not write in this space.

Place a sheet of scrap paper here and write your answers on that.

Always remember to time yourself for each test.

Write your score out of 20 and your time in minutes and seconds on the Record Sheet at the back of this book.

Test 12a

1 9 + 7 = *

2 7 + 8 = *

3 7 + 7 = *

4 4 + 12 = *

5 11 + 5 = *

6 11 + 7 = *

7 2 + 13 = *

8 8 + 9 = *

9 9 + 5 = *

10 12 + 4 = *

11 6 + 11 = *

12 14 + 3 = *

13 9 + 8 = *

14 13 + 5 = *

15 11 + 6 = *

16 7 + 11 = *

17 14 + 5 = *

18 12 + 7 = *

19 4 + 15 = *

20 12 + 6 = *

Do not write in this space.

Place a sheet of scrap paper here and write your answers on that.

Always remember to time yourself for each test.

Write your score out of 20 and your time in minutes and seconds on the Record Sheet at the back of this book.

Test 12b

1 14 − 7 = *

2 16 − 11 = *

3 17 − 9 = *

4 17 − 11 = *

5 16 − 4 = *

6 15 − 8 = *

7 17 − 14 = *

8 19 − 7 = *

9 17 − 6 = *

10 18 − 12 = *

11 19 − 5 = *

12 18 − 7 = *

13 15 − 2 = *

14 17 − 8 = *

15 18 − 11 = *

16 19 − 4 = *

17 14 − 9 = *

18 16 − 7 = *

19 16 − 12 = *

20 18 − 5 = *

Do not write in this space.

Place a sheet of scrap paper here and write your answers on that.

Always remember to time yourself for each test.

Write your score out of 20 and your time in minutes and seconds on the Record Sheet at the back of this book.

Test 12c

1 $* + 7 = 18$

2 $17 - * = 14$

3 $5 + * = 16$

4 $* - 9 = 8$

5 $* + 5 = 19$

6 $18 - * = 6$

7 $2 + * = 15$

8 $* - 7 = 8$

9 $* + 12 = 16$

10 $14 - * = 5$

11 $11 + * = 16$

12 $* - 4 = 15$

13 $* + 7 = 14$

14 $17 - * = 8$

15 $13 + * = 18$

16 $* - 7 = 9$

17 $* + 4 = 16$

18 $19 - * = 12$

19 $7 + * = 18$

20 $* - 12 = 4$

Do not write in
this space.

Place a sheet of
scrap paper here
and write your
answers on that.

Always remember
to time yourself
for each test.

Write your score
out of 20 and
your time in
minutes and
seconds on the
Record Sheet
at the back of
this book.

Test 13a

1. $3 + 11 = *$

2. $10 + 8 = *$

3. $13 + 6 = *$

4. $9 + 6 = *$

5. $13 + 3 = *$

6. $15 + 4 = *$

7. $12 + 2 = *$

8. $8 + 9 = *$

9. $3 + 15 = *$

10. $14 + 4 = *$

11. $3 + 12 = *$

12. $13 + 4 = *$

13. $16 + 2 = *$

14. $9 + 9 = *$

15. $8 + 11 = *$

16. $10 + 5 = *$

17. $12 + 3 = *$

18. $10 + 10 = *$

19. $12 + 5 = *$

20. $16 + 3 = *$

Do not write in this space.

Place a sheet of scrap paper here and write your answers on that.

Always remember to time yourself for each test.

Write your score out of 20 and your time in minutes and seconds on the Record Sheet at the back of this book.

Test 13b

1. $15 - 3 = *$

2. $17 - 9 = *$

3. $15 - 6 = *$

4. $14 - 11 = *$

5. $19 - 8 = *$

6. $20 - 10 = *$

7. $18 - 2 = *$

8. $18 - 15 = *$

9. $16 - 3 = *$

10. $18 - 10 = *$

11. $15 - 10 = *$

12. $18 - 9 = *$

13. $17 - 12 = *$

14. $14 - 2 = *$

15. $19 - 15 = *$

16. $18 - 14 = *$

17. $19 - 3 = *$

18. $15 - 12 = *$

19. $19 - 6 = *$

20. $17 - 4 = *$

Do not write in
this space.

Place a sheet of
scrap paper here
and write your
answers on that.

Always remember
to time yourself
for each test.

Write your score
out of 20 and
your time in
minutes and
seconds on the
Record Sheet
at the back of
this book.

Test 13c

1   * + 15 = 18

2   19 − * = 6

3   3 + * = 15

4   * − 5 = 12

5   * + 4 = 19

6   14 − * = 2

7   4 + * = 18

8   * − 8 = 9

9   * + 6 = 15

10   18 − * = 9

11   3 + * = 14

12   * − 10 = 10

13   * + 3 = 19

14   19 − * = 11

15   2 + * = 18

16   * − 3 = 12

17   * + 10 = 15

18   16 − * = 13

19   13 + * = 17

20   * − 10 = 8

Do not write in this space.

Place a sheet of scrap paper here and write your answers on that.

Always remember to time yourself for each test.

Write your score out of 20 and your time in minutes and seconds on the Record Sheet at the back of this book.

Test 14a

1. $2 + 14 = *$

2. $9 + 5 = *$

3. $5 + 12 = *$

4. $11 + 6 = *$

5. $10 + 10 = *$

6. $17 + 2 = *$

7. $15 + 3 = *$

8. $8 + 7 = *$

9. $5 + 14 = *$

10. $13 + 7 = *$

11. $15 + 2 = *$

12. $12 + 6 = *$

13. $16 + 4 = *$

14. $12 + 2 = *$

15. $4 + 13 = *$

16. $8 + 12 = *$

17. $11 + 8 = *$

18. $5 + 9 = *$

19. $14 + 6 = *$

20. $9 + 8 = *$

Do not write in this space.

Place a sheet of scrap paper here and write your answers on that.

Always remember to time yourself for each test.

Write your score out of 20 and your time in minutes and seconds on the Record Sheet at the back of this book.

Test 14b

1. $20 - 10 = *$

2. $17 - 15 = *$

3. $14 - 2 = *$

4. $19 - 8 = *$

5. $17 - 5 = *$

6. $16 - 14 = *$

7. $20 - 4 = *$

8. $17 - 13 = *$

9. $14 - 9 = *$

10. $20 - 12 = *$

11. $17 - 6 = *$

12. $18 - 12 = *$

13. $20 - 6 = *$

14. $17 - 8 = *$

15. $18 - 15 = *$

16. $14 - 5 = *$

17. $19 - 2 = *$

18. $20 - 7 = *$

19. $15 - 8 = *$

20. $19 - 14 = *$

Do not write in this space.

Place a sheet of scrap paper here and write your answers on that.

Always remember to time yourself for each test.

Write your score out of 20 and your time in minutes and seconds on the Record Sheet at the back of this book.

Test 14c

1. $* + 5 = 14$

2. $20 - * = 13$

3. $15 + * = 18$

4. $* - 4 = 16$

5. $* + 2 = 17$

6. $20 - * = 8$

7. $10 + * = 20$

8. $* - 9 = 5$

9. $* + 6 = 20$

10. $17 - * = 8$

11. $11 + * = 17$

12. $* - 7 = 8$

13. $* + 11 = 19$

14. $18 - * = 12$

15. $5 + * = 19$

16. $* - 4 = 13$

17. $* + 2 = 16$

18. $17 - * = 5$

19. $2 + * = 14$

20. $* - 2 = 17$

Test 15a

1 2 + 15 = *

2 6 + 13 = *

3 9 + 11 = *

4 13 + 5 = *

5 8 + 10 = *

6 6 + 9 = *

7 3 + 14 = *

8 5 + 15 = *

9 11 + 3 = *

10 16 + 2 = *

11 11 + 9 = *

12 12 + 4 = *

13 12 + 8 = *

14 2 + 16 = *

15 15 + 5 = *

16 9 + 10 = *

17 14 + 2 = *

18 6 + 14 = *

19 3 + 13 = *

20 18 + 2 = *

Do not write in this space.

Place a sheet of scrap paper here and write your answers on that.

Always remember to time yourself for each test.

Write your score out of 20 and your time in minutes and seconds on the Record Sheet at the back of this book.

Test 15b

1   20 − 11 = *

2   14 − 3 = *

3   16 − 12 = *

4   20 − 15 = *

5   20 − 6 = *

6   16 − 3 = *

7   18 − 5 = *

8   17 − 2 = *

9   20 − 8 = *

10   18 − 2 = *

11   20 − 9 = *

12   15 − 6 = *

13   19 − 10 = *

14   20 − 2 = *

15   16 − 14 = *

16   18 − 2 = *

17   17 − 14 = *

18   18 − 10 = *

19   19 − 6 = *

20   20 − 5 = *

Do not write in
this space.

Place a sheet of
scrap paper here
and write your
answers on that.

Always remember
to time yourself
for each test.

Write your score
out of 20 and
your time in
minutes and
seconds on the
Record Sheet
at the back of
this book.

Test 15c

1. $* + 2 = 20$

2. $15 - * = 9$

3. $9 + * = 20$

4. $* - 5 = 13$

5. $* + 8 = 20$

6. $19 - * = 10$

7. $2 + * = 17$

8. $* - 6 = 14$

9. $* + 14 = 17$

10. $18 - * = 2$

11. $2 + * = 18$

12. $* - 9 = 11$

13. $* + 3 = 14$

14. $19 - * = 6$

15. $5 + * = 20$

16. $* - 4 = 12$

17. $* + 3 = 16$

18. $20 - * = 5$

19. $8 + * = 18$

20. $* - 2 = 14$

Do not write in this space.

Place a sheet of scrap paper here and write your answers on that.

Always remember to time yourself for each test.

Write your score out of 20 and your time in minutes and seconds on the Record Sheet at the back of this book.

Test 16a

1 11 + 4 = *

2 13 + 6 = *

3 7 + 13 = *

4 7 + 11 = *

5 3 + 16 = *

6 8 + 8 = *

7 17 + 3 = *

8 4 + 14 = *

9 2 + 12 = *

10 8 + 11 = *

11 4 + 16 = *

12 6 + 12 = *

13 2 + 17 = *

14 7 + 8 = *

15 12 + 7 = *

16 14 + 4 = *

17 14 + 2 = *

18 19 + 1 = *

19 11 + 5 = *

20 14 + 5 = *

Do not write in this space.

Place a sheet of scrap paper here and write your answers on that.

Always remember to time yourself for each test.

Write your score out of 20 and your time in minutes and seconds on the Record Sheet at the back of this book.

Test 16b

1   16 – 8 = *

2   14 – 12 = *

3   18 – 6 = *

4   18 – 4 = *

5   19 – 7 = *

6   19 – 13 = *

7   20 – 13 = *

8   16 – 14 = *

9   20 – 4 = *

10   16 – 11 = *

11   19 – 5 = *

12   20 – 1 = *

13   19 – 2 = *

14   18 – 7 = *

15   15 – 11 = *

16   15 – 8 = *

17   19 – 11 = *

18   20 – 7 = *

19   18 – 14 = *

20   19 – 3 = *

Do not write in
this space.

Place a sheet of
scrap paper here
and write your
answers on that.

Always remember
to time yourself
for each test.

Write your score
out of 20 and
your time in
minutes and
seconds on the
Record Sheet
at the back of
this book.

Test 16c

1. $* + 16 = 19$

2. $14 - * = 12$

3. $7 + * = 18$

4. $* - 8 = 7$

5. $* + 4 = 20$

6. $18 - * = 14$

7. $8 + * = 19$

8. $* - 6 = 12$

9. $* + 5 = 16$

10. $19 - * = 14$

11. $7 + * = 20$

12. $* - 6 = 13$

13. $* + 2 = 19$

14. $18 - * = 14$

15. $8 + * = 16$

16. $* - 3 = 17$

17. $* + 7 = 19$

18. $15 - * = 4$

19. $1 + * = 20$

20. $* - 14 = 2$

Do not write in this space.

Place a sheet of scrap paper here and write your answers on that.

Always remember to time yourself for each test.

Write your score out of 20 and your time in minutes and seconds on the Record Sheet at the back of this book.

Test 17a

1   14 + 6 = *

2   11 + 6 = *

3   13 + 5 = *

4   18 + 2 = *

5   13 + 7 = *

6   6 + 8 = *

7   5 + 4 = *

8   4 + 15 = *

9   15 + 2 = *

10   16 + 3 = *

11   8 + 12 = *

12   7 + 8 = *

13   13 + 2 = *

14   11 + 3 = *

15   10 + 9 = *

16   15 + 5 = *

17   6 + 7 = *

18   4 + 16 = *

19   11 + 7 = *

20   9 + 11 = *

Do not write in
this space.

Place a sheet of
scrap paper here
and write your
answers on that.

Always remember
to time yourself
for each test.

Write your score
out of 20 and
your time in
minutes and
seconds on the
Record Sheet
at the back of
this book.

Test 17b

1 20 − 8 = *

2 18 − 5 = *

3 19 − 15 = *

4 14 − 6 = *

5 19 − 3 = *

6 13 − 7 = *

7 20 − 16 = *

8 18 − 7 = *

9 17 − 5 = *

10 20 − 7 = *

11 17 − 11 = *

12 20 − 14 = *

13 14 − 3 = *

14 15 − 8 = *

15 20 − 15 = *

16 20 − 11 = *

17 9 − 5 = *

18 19 − 10 = *

19 15 − 13 = *

20 20 − 2 = *

Do not write in
this space.

Place a sheet of
scrap paper here
and write your
answers on that.

Always remember
to time yourself
for each test.

Write your score
out of 20 and
your time in
minutes and
seconds on the
Record Sheet
at the back of
this book.

Test 17c

1   $* + 4 = 19$

2   $20 - * = 13$

3   $16 + * = 19$

4   $* - 6 = 7$

5   $* + 4 = 9$

6   $19 - * = 10$

7   $7 + * = 15$

8   $* - 9 = 11$

9   $* + 6 = 17$

10 $14 - * = 6$

11 $8 + * = 20$

12 $* - 6 = 14$

13 $* + 7 = 18$

14 $20 - * = 2$

15 $11 + * = 14$

16 $* - 14 = 6$

17 $* + 5 = 18$

18 $17 - * = 15$

19 $5 + * = 20$

20 $* - 13 = 2$

Do not write in this space.

Place a sheet of scrap paper here and write your answers on that.

Always remember to time yourself for each test.

Write your score out of 20 and your time in minutes and seconds on the Record Sheet at the back of this book.

Test 18a

1 16 + 4 = *

2 5 + 13 = *

3 7 + 12 = *

4 12 + 5 = *

5 13 + 4 = *

6 15 + 4 = *

7 13 + 3 = *

8 7 + 13 = *

9 14 + 3 = *

10 5 + 11 = *

11 17 + 2 = *

12 11 + 9 = *

13 5 + 6 = *

14 7 + 4 = *

15 8 + 7 = *

16 9 + 9 = *

17 12 + 8 = *

18 2 + 15 = *

19 6 + 14 = *

20 8 + 6 = *

Do not write in
this space.

Place a sheet of
scrap paper here
and write your
answers on that.

Always remember
to time yourself
for each test.

Write your score
out of 20 and
your time in
minutes and
seconds on the
Record Sheet
at the back of
this book.

Test 18b

1. $17 - 4 = *$
2. $16 - 11 = *$
3. $20 - 9 = *$
4. $11 - 4 = *$
5. $20 - 13 = *$
6. $17 - 14 = *$
7. $19 - 7 = *$
8. $15 - 8 = *$
9. $20 - 12 = *$
10. $14 - 6 = *$
11. $20 - 6 = *$
12. $18 - 9 = *$
13. $19 - 2 = *$
14. $16 - 13 = *$
15. $17 - 12 = *$
16. $11 - 5 = *$
17. $17 - 2 = *$
18. $19 - 4 = *$
19. $20 - 16 = *$
20. $18 - 5 = *$

Do not write in this space.

Place a sheet of scrap paper here and write your answers on that.

Always remember to time yourself for each test.

Write your score out of 20 and your time in minutes and seconds on the Record Sheet at the back of this book.

Test 18c

1 $* + 6 = 20$

2 $16 - * = 11$

3 $7 + * = 19$

4 $* - 4 = 7$

5 $* + 5 = 18$

6 $14 - * = 8$

7 $13 + * = 17$

8 $* - 8 = 12$

9 $* + 3 = 17$

10 $20 - * = 13$

11 $11 + * = 20$

12 $* - 5 = 12$

13 $* + 7 = 15$

14 $18 - * = 9$

15 $13 + * = 16$

16 $* - 4 = 15$

17 $* + 4 = 20$

18 $19 - * = 17$

19 $2 + * = 17$

20 $* - 5 = 6$

Do not write in
this space.

Place a sheet of
scrap paper here
and write your
answers on that.

Always remember
to time yourself
for each test.

Write your score
out of 20 and
your time in
minutes and
seconds on the
Record Sheet
at the back of
this book.

Test 19a

1. $90 + 40 = *$

2. $140 + 60 = *$

3. $130 + 40 = *$

4. $80 + 50 = *$

5. $70 + 90 = *$

6. $130 + 70 = *$

7. $90 + 60 = *$

8. $120 + 70 = *$

9. $80 + 110 = *$

10. $90 + 30 = *$

11. $140 + 50 = *$

12. $90 + 80 = *$

13. $110 + 70 = *$

14. $50 + 80 = *$

15. $40 + 70 = *$

16. $80 + 80 = *$

17. $80 + 120 = *$

18. $70 + 70 = *$

19. $90 + 70 = *$

20. $80 + 40 = *$

Do not write in
this space.

Place a sheet of
scrap paper here
and write your
answers on that.

Always remember
to time yourself
for each test.

Write your score
out of 20 and
your time in
minutes and
seconds on the
Record Sheet
at the back of
this book.

Test 19b

1. $130 - 50 = *$

2. $150 - 90 = *$

3. $120 - 30 = *$

4. $180 - 110 = *$

5. $200 - 130 = *$

6. $160 - 80 = *$

7. $180 - 110 = *$

8. $190 - 70 = *$

9. $160 - 70 = *$

10. $120 - 80 = *$

11. $110 - 70 = *$

12. $130 - 80 = *$

13. $200 - 60 = *$

14. $130 - 90 = *$

15. $160 - 70 = *$

16. $170 - 130 = *$

17. $200 - 80 = *$

18. $170 - 90 = *$

19. $140 - 70 = *$

20. $190 - 110 = *$

Do not write in this space.

Place a sheet of scrap paper here and write your answers on that.

Always remember to time yourself for each test.

Write your score out of 20 and your time in minutes and seconds on the Record Sheet at the back of this book.

Test 19c

1. $* + 90 = 160$

2. $130 - * = 50$

3. $70 + * = 190$

4. $* - 40 = 80$

5. $* + 60 = 200$

6. $170 - * = 80$

7. $90 + * = 150$

8. $* - 70 = 90$

9. $* + 40 = 130$

10. $190 - * = 80$

11. $90 + * = 120$

12. $* - 40 = 70$

13. $* + 80 = 200$

14. $180 - * = 70$

15. $80 + * = 130$

16. $* - 80 = 80$

17. $* + 70 = 200$

18. $180 - * = 110$

19. $70 + * = 140$

20. $* - 50 = 140$

Do not write in this space.

Place a sheet of scrap paper here and write your answers on that.

Always remember to time yourself for each test.

Write your score out of 20 and your time in minutes and seconds on the Record Sheet at the back of this book.

Test 20a

1 $50 + 70 = *$

2 $40 + 90 = *$

3 $120 + 80 = *$

4 $140 + 40 = *$

5 $60 + 90 = *$

6 $80 + 50 = *$

7 $40 + 80 = *$

8 $30 + 160 = *$

9 $80 + 90 = *$

10 $70 + 120 = *$

11 $70 + 40 = *$

12 $60 + 70 = *$

13 $120 + 30 = *$

14 $80 + 30 = *$

15 $90 + 40 = *$

16 $130 + 60 = *$

17 $40 + 50 = *$

18 $110 + 90 = *$

19 $70 + 80 = *$

20 $60 + 60 = *$

Do not write in
this space.

Place a sheet of
scrap paper here
and write your
answers on that.

Always remember
to time yourself
for each test.

Write your score
out of 20 and
your time in
minutes and
seconds on the
Record Sheet
at the back of
this book.

Test 20b

1. $130 - 60 = *$

2. $190 - 160 = *$

3. $120 - 40 = *$

4. $150 - 60 = *$

5. $200 - 80 = *$

6. $110 - 30 = *$

7. $200 - 90 = *$

8. $120 - 60 = *$

9. $190 - 130 = *$

10. $190 - 70 = *$

11. $150 - 30 = *$

12. $120 - 70 = *$

13. $130 - 40 = *$

14. $150 - 70 = *$

15. $90 - 40 = *$

16. $110 - 70 = *$

17. $170 - 90 = *$

18. $140 - 80 = *$

19. $180 - 40 = *$

20. $130 - 90 = *$

Do not write in
this space.

Place a sheet of
scrap paper here
and write your
answers on that.

Always remember
to time yourself
for each test.

Write your score
out of 20 and
your time in
minutes and
seconds on the
Record Sheet
at the back of
this book.

Test 20c

1 $* + 80 = 200$

2 $190 - * = 70$

3 $40 + * = 130$

4 $* - 80 = 70$

5 $* + 70 = 130$

6 $120 - * = 60$

7 $40 + * = 110$

8 $* - 60 = 90$

9 $* + 70 = 120$

10 $170 - * = 90$

11 $80 + * = 110$

12 $* - 90 = 110$

13 $* + 50 = 90$

14 $120 - * = 80$

15 $90 + * = 130$

16 $* - 130 = 60$

17 $* + 30 = 150$

18 $190 - * = 160$

19 $40 + * = 180$

20 $* - 50 = 80$

Do not write in this space.

Place a sheet of scrap paper here and write your answers on that.

Always remember to time yourself for each test.

Write your score out of 20 and your time in minutes and seconds on the Record Sheet at the back of this book.

Record Sheet

Date	Test No.	Time	Score

Record Sheet

Date	Test No.	Time	Score

Record Sheet

Date	Test No.	Time	Score